Brilliant Brain Coloring Book

fanciful brain designs

 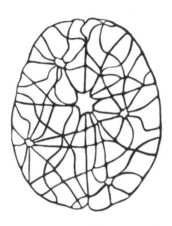 

by
Laura Bundesen
LauraBundesen.com

Brilliant Brain Coloring Book
Copyright© 2020 by Laura Bundesen

ISBN: 978-0-9652460-1-9

Share your coloring pages on social media with
#brilliantbraincoloring

Tag the artist on Instagram and Twitter @LauraBundesen
Facebook @LauraBundesen.Artist

This coloring book may be ordered directly from
Laura Bundesen
LauraBundesen.com
P.O. Box 89, Huntington, MA 01050

LauraBundesen.com
#brilliantbraincoloring

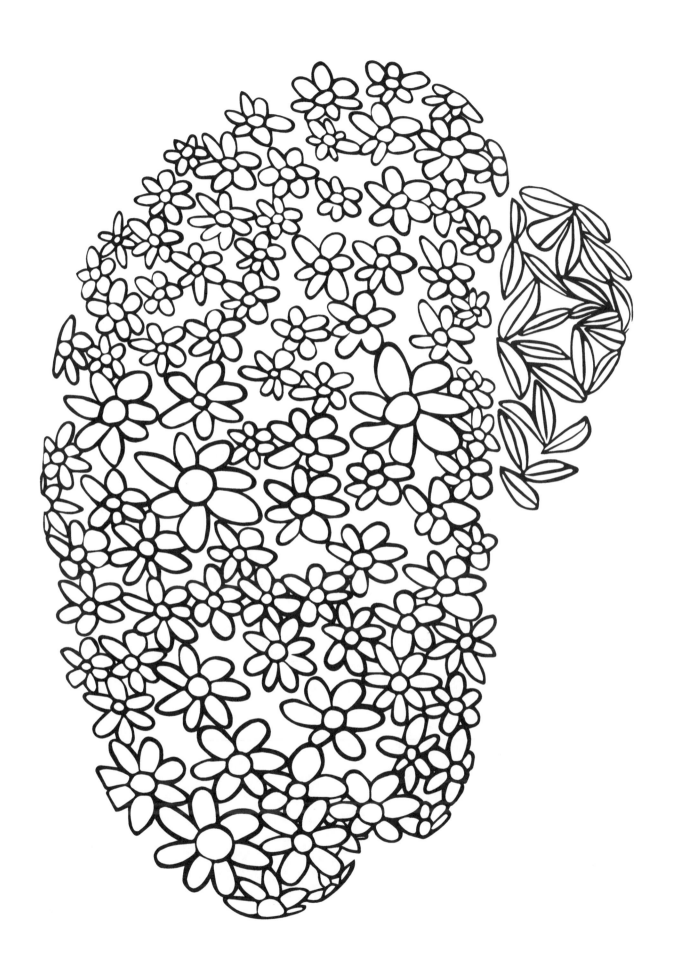

LauraBundesen.com
#brilliantbraincoloring

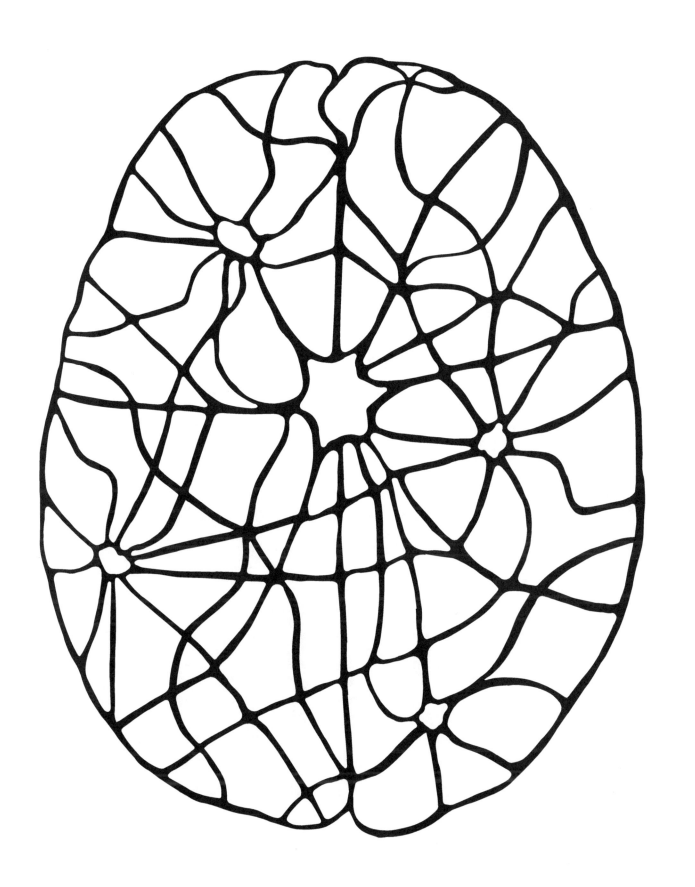

LauraBundesen.com
#brilliantbraincoloring

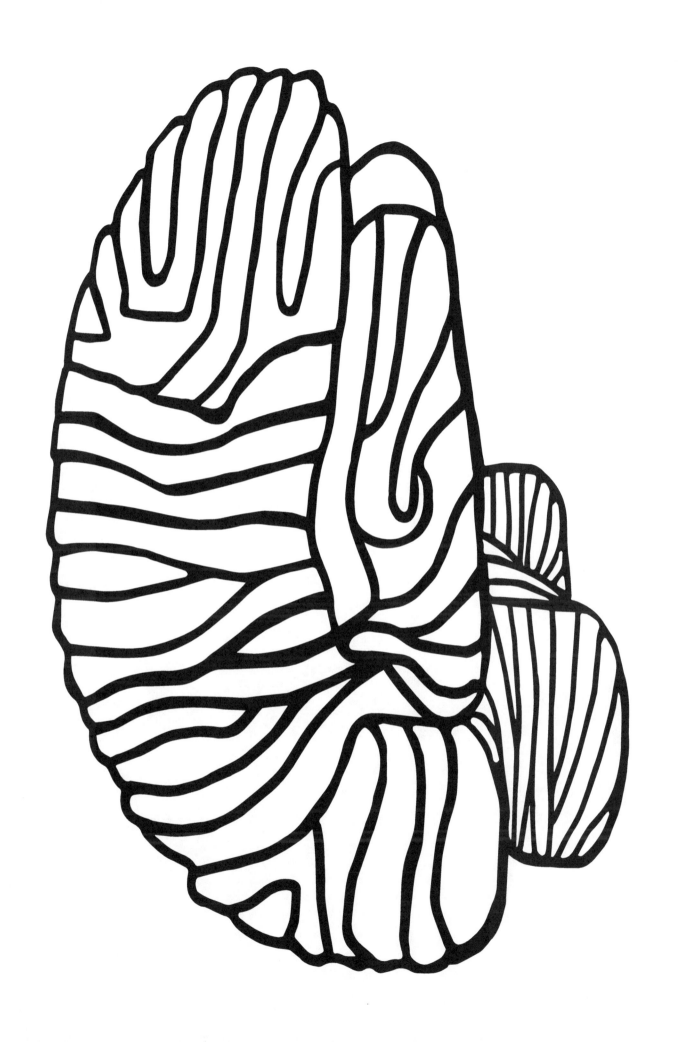

LauraBundesen.com
#brilliantbraincoloring

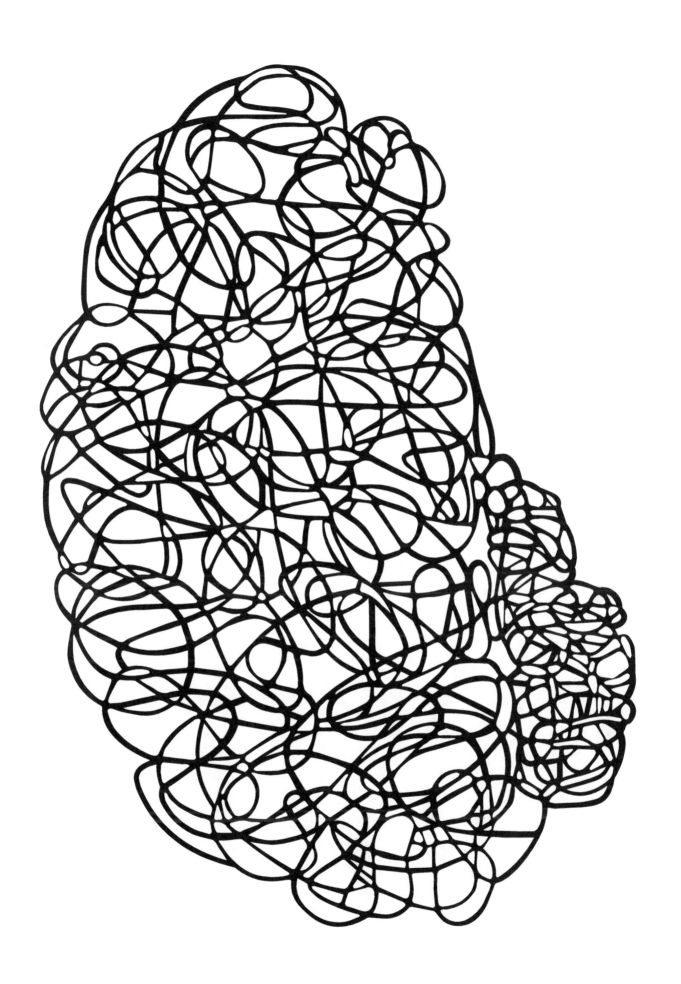

LauraBundesen.com
#brilliantbraincoloring

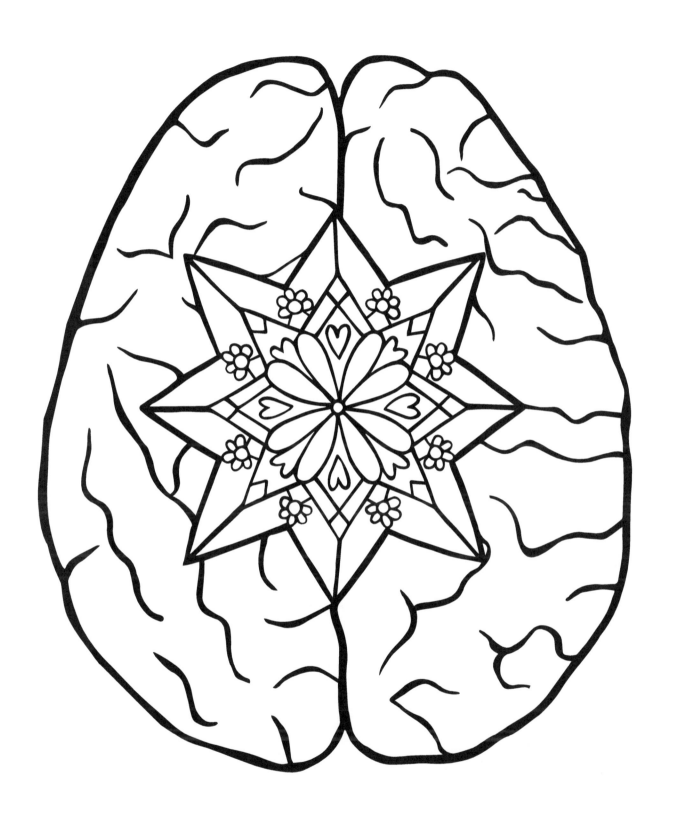

LauraBundesen.com
#brilliantbraincoloring

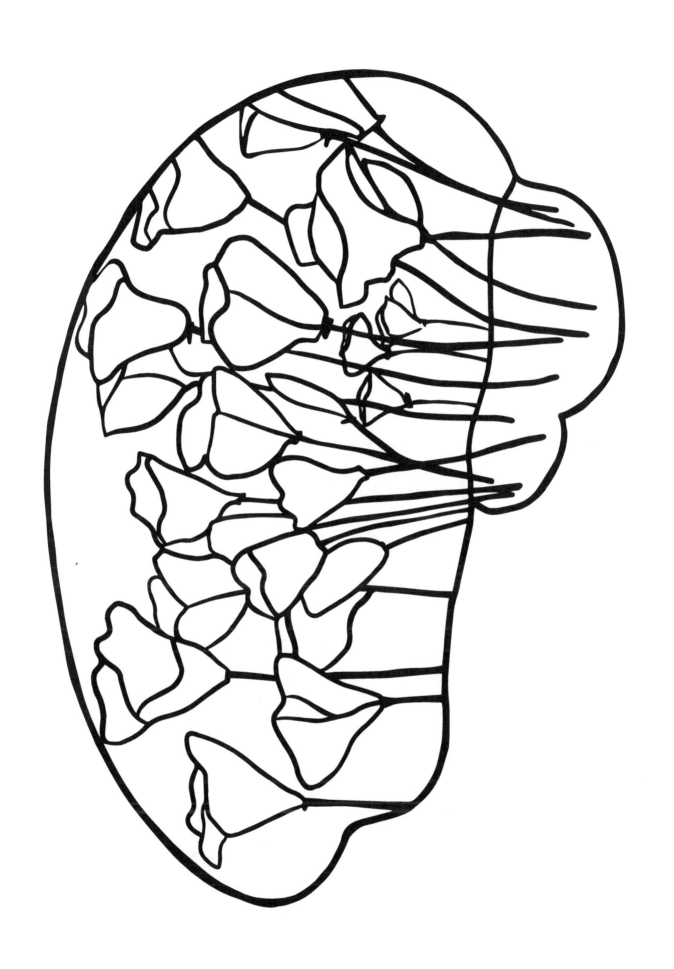

LauraBundesen.com
#brilliantbraincoloring

LauraBundesen.com
#brilliantbraincoloring

LauraBundesen.com
#brilliantbraincoloring

LauraBundesen.com
#brilliantbraincoloring

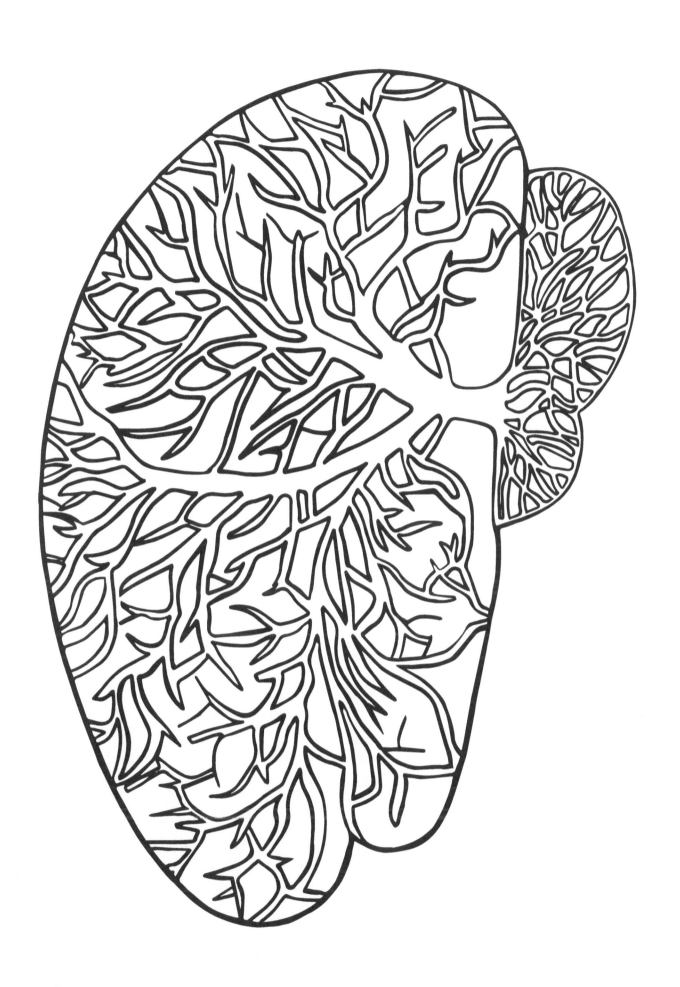

LauraBundesen.com
#brilliantbraincoloring

LauraBundesen.com
#brilliantbraincoloring

LauraBundesen.com
#brilliantbraincoloring

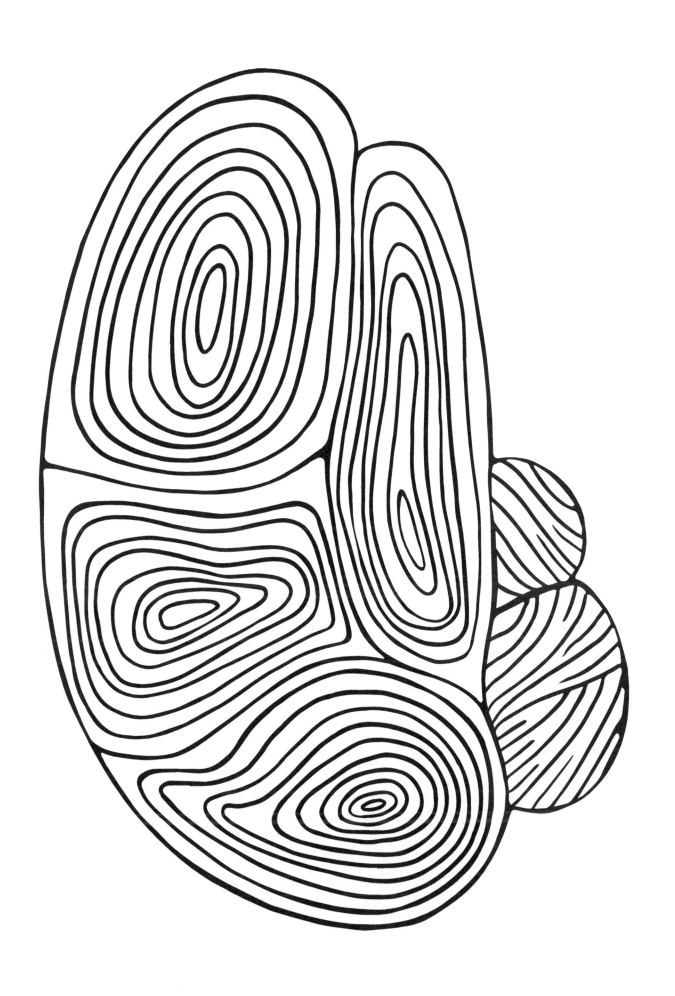

LauraBundesen.com
#brilliantbraincoloring

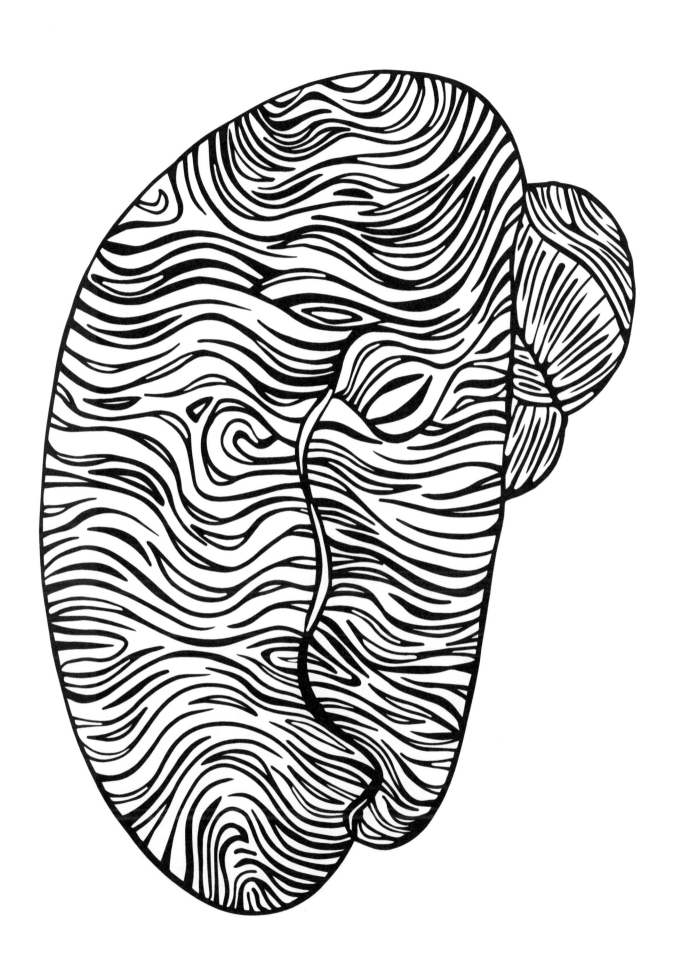

LauraBundesen.com
#brilliantbraincoloring

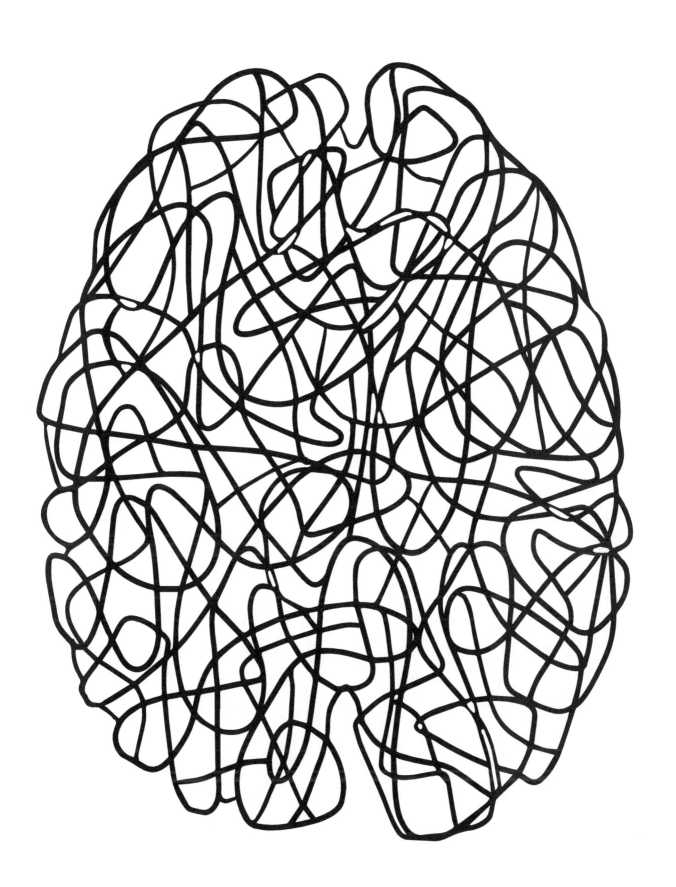

LauraBundesen.com
#brilliantbraincoloring

LauraBundesen.com
#brilliantbraincoloring

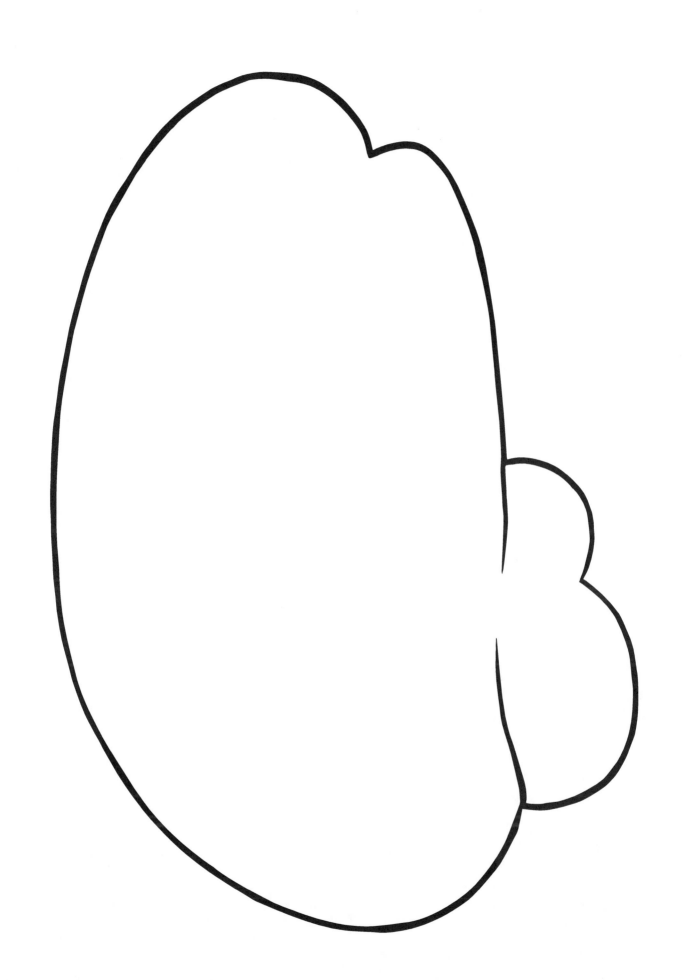

LauraBundesen.com
#brilliantbraincoloring

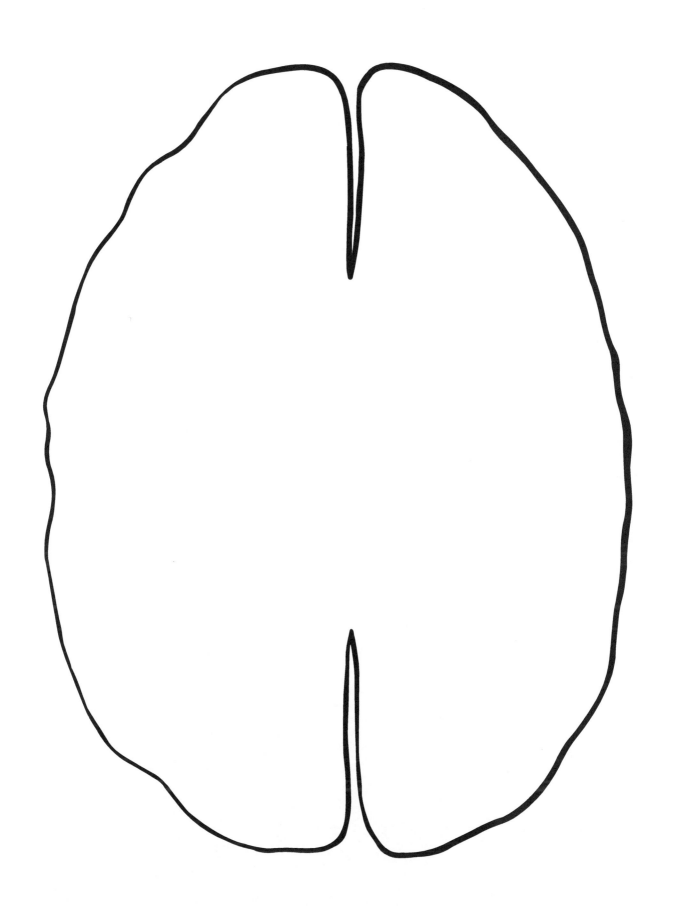

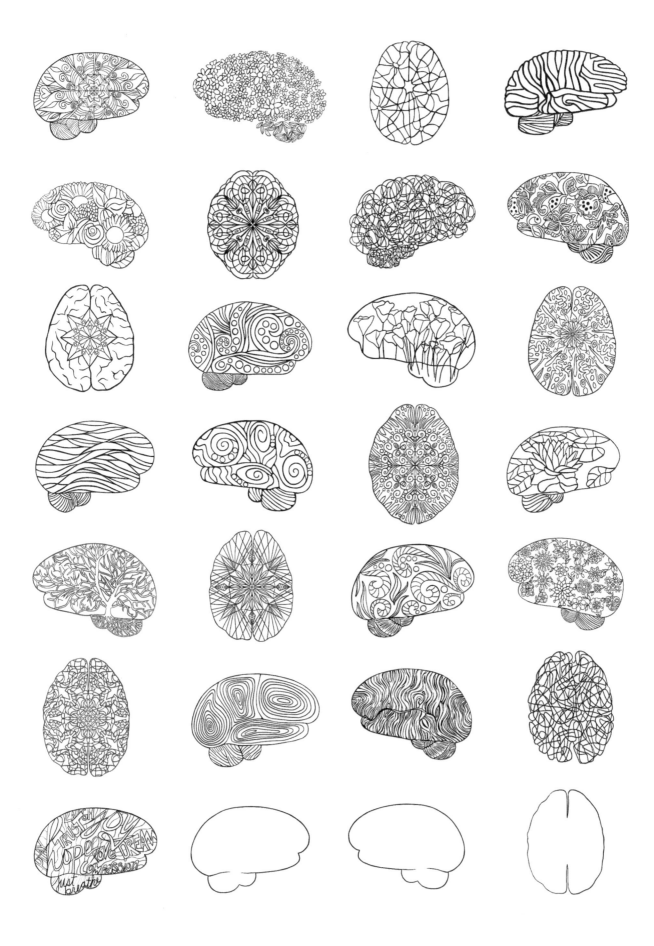

LauraBundesen.com
#brilliantbraincoloring

Made in United States
Troutdale, OR
12/14/2023

1588572626R00038